After the seeming final defeat of the Sith, the Republic enters a state of complacency. In the waning years of the Republic, the Senate rife with corruption, the ambitious Senator Palpatine causes himself to be elected Supreme Chancellor. This is the era of the prequel trilogy.

The events in this story take place approximately two years before the Battle of Yavin.

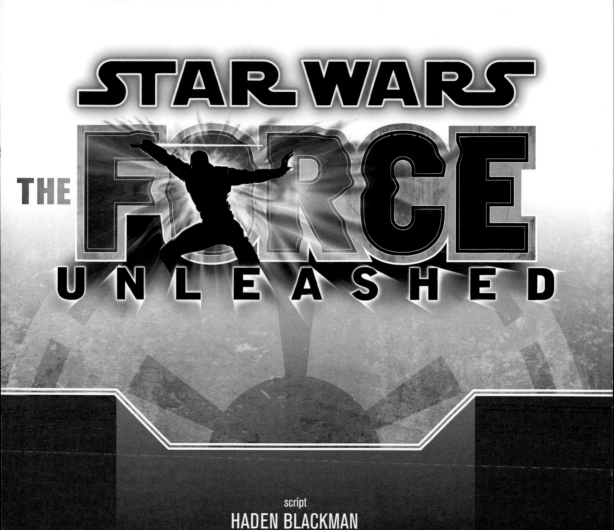

STAR WARS
THE FORCE UNLEASHED

script
HADEN BLACKMAN

publisher
MIKE RICHARDSON

collection designer
SCOTT COOK

art director
LIA RIBACCHI

editor
RANDY STRADLEY

assistant editors
FREDDYE LINS and DAVE MARSHALL

special thanks to Elaine Mederer, Jann Moorhead, David Anderman,
Leland Chee, Sue Rostoni, and Carol Roeder at Lucas Licensing,
and Brett Rector at LucasArts

STAR WARS: THE FORCE UNLEASHED

Published by
Dark Horse Books
A division of Dark Horse Comics, Inc.
10956 SE Main Street
Milwaukie, OR 97222

darkhorse.com
starwars.com

To find a comics shop in your area, call the Comic Shop Locator Service toll-free at
1-888-266-4226

Scholastic Edition: January 2009

ISBN 978-1-59582-334-2

Printed in China

INTRODUCTION

I used to think that true terror was the slow-motion seconds before a car crash, or the breath-stealing instant when you realize you're falling off of a ladder, or even the gut-wrenching discovery of squealing rats in the attic. But, for me, those moments pale compared to the beautiful morning in spring of 2005 when—surrounded by the idyllic scenery of Skywalker Ranch—I found myself standing in front of George Lucas, attempting to relate a key concept behind a new *Star Wars* video game being developed at LucasArts. Here I was, little more than a mere fan of the *Star Wars* mythos, describing to the father of all things *Star Wars* our vision for the Force as a primal energy that would be portrayed in-game as "over the top," "amped up," and even "out of control." Describing, in essence, "the Force *unleashed*."

For months, the development team at LucasArts had been working on the basic concepts for what would become *The Force Unleashed*—now considered the next chapter in the *Star Wars* Saga. We had generated dozens of pieces of concept art, several animation tests, and hundreds of pages of design documentation to support our ideas. We had even begun the difficult process of developing and integrating cutting-edge technologies that would allow us to deliver on our vision of "the Force unleashed." Even early on, we strongly believed that using the Force

in new and dramatic ways would provide a compelling gameplay experience, but I also knew that if George Lucas disagreed with this "reimagining" of the Force, our team would be scrambling to find a new direction.

So, back to being completely terrified . . . Fortunately, during my presentation to Lucas, I did not need to rely on words alone. The team had created a short "previsualization" video that captured the essence of "the Force unleashed" through a series of brief animations depicting an anonymous Force wielder violently pushing, repelling, and throwing stormtroopers around—doing the kinds of things you'll see in the pages of this graphic novel. We showed this video to Lucas (twice, if I recall correctly), after which he looked up and said: "That's perfect for a game. Go make *that*."

But a *Star Wars* experience—and certainly one attempting to become the next *chapter* in the *Star Wars* saga—is not simply about action or even the Force. We also needed a strong central character, and a captivating story. Over the next two hours, I walked Lucas through our proposed storyline—a tale of Darth Vader's secret apprentice, who begins on a quest to kill the last of the Jedi but ultimately ends up battling "dark Jedi" in an attempt to save Princess Leia and redeem himself for his past actions. And that's when the trouble really began . . .

I knew walking into the meeting that Lucas might balk at some of our story ideas, but ironically, the "big ideas" about which I was most worried didn't cause much debate. Lucas approved our desire to cast the player in the role of Darth Vader's secret apprentice. He even spent a great deal of time describing how Vader would motivate his apprentice (through fear and a promise of overthrowing the Emperor together). He approved the story's setting between Episodes III and IV, a time period that had previously been largely off limits, and offered us great insight into the political events of that era. Even ideas that we ultimately felt were too outlandish and would eventually drop from the story—such as the notion that the apprentice might commune with the spirit of Qui-Gon Jinn or Mace Windu—weren't rejected.

However, Lucas did have three major concerns about the story that would dramatically alter our plot. First, he was not comfortable with Princess Leia being protected by the Apprentice. Second, he felt that the Emperor—who never made an appearance in our original draft—needed to have a much larger presence in the game. And third (and perhaps most important), he was adamant that we needed to populate our story with *new* characters who fulfilled familiar *Star Wars* archetypes in new ways, characters who would later become a Jedi mentor who transforms from a militant general to a blind drunk,

yet still manages to teach the Apprentice something about the Force; a comic sidekick who is as dangerous as he is naïve, and proves that even Darth Vader's apprentice can feel friendship and loyalty; and a love interest who is just as conflicted as the Apprentice, but ultimately inspires him to become a hero.

Lucas's direction at this meeting (and many others) allowed us to take a mediocre story and shape it into the next chapter of the *Star Wars* saga. And I've now had the double good fortune of being able to adapt that story into this graphic novel, allowing the events to unfold from the points of view of some of our original characters.

The *Star Wars* universe is George Lucas's toybox, but I'll always be grateful that he took the time to share his toys with us, and to tell us how to squeeze the most fun and excitement out of each and every one. And hopefully, we've been able to add a few new toys to that box that others can play with too.

Haden Blackman
January 2008

PROXY recording 91608.

The historical records will claim that the Rebel Alliance was born on Corellia. That *is* a documented fact. But the *truth* is this:

The Rebel Alliance was born somewhere in the Scarl system...

...aboard *Darth Vader's* personal starship, the *Executor*.

DO YOU KNOW WHY YOU'RE HERE?

MY ORDERS ARE CLEAR. I AM TO KEEP YOUR SHIP RUNNING AND FLY YOU WHEREVER YOUR MISSIONS REQUIRE.

DID VADER TELL YOU THAT HE KILLED OUR LAST PILOT?

NO, BUT I CAN ONLY ASSUME THAT HE GAVE LORD VADER GOOD CAUSE TO DO SO. I WILL NOT.

LET'S HOPE SO. I'M SICK OF TRAINING NEW PILOTS.

WHAT IS THIS?!? WHAT HAVE YOU DONE TO MY SHIP?

I'VE TAKEN THE LIBERTY OF UPGRADING THE *ROGUE SHADOW'S* SENSOR ARRAY.

NOW YOU'LL BE ABLE TO SPY ON ANY SUSPECT SHIPS ACROSS AN ENTIRE SYSTEM.

My Master tore through that shipyard...

...using everything Vader had taught him --

-- and some maneuvers he invented himself.

And as Vader commanded, he left no witnesses.

And eventually, he reached Master Kota...

My Master's next mission was to kill *Shaak Ti.*

A hero from the Clone Wars...

...one of the Order's most cunning warriors, who had disappeared, vanished.

But we would find her...

...on the fungus world Felucia.

ASSASSINS.

Fortunately, my Master had some experience battling monsters.

KRRRASSH!

41

BOOOOOM!

...she could not hold Starkiller, No one could...

I PROMISED DARTH VADER I WOULD NOT FAIL HIM.

UNGH!

THEN YOU ARE VADER'S SLAVE. BUT YOUR POWER IS WASTED WITH HIM. YOU COULD BE SO MUCH MORE.

Vader was pleased with Starkiller's mission to Felucia. With Shaak Ti's death, it appeared that my Master would at least achieve *his* primary programming -- to stand at Vader's side against the Emperor.

THE EMPEROR'S FLEET HAS ARRIVED.

YOU LURED HIM HERE TO US? WHEN DO WE STRIKE?

I DID NOT SUMMON HIM.

HIS SPIES FOLLOWED YOU HERE.

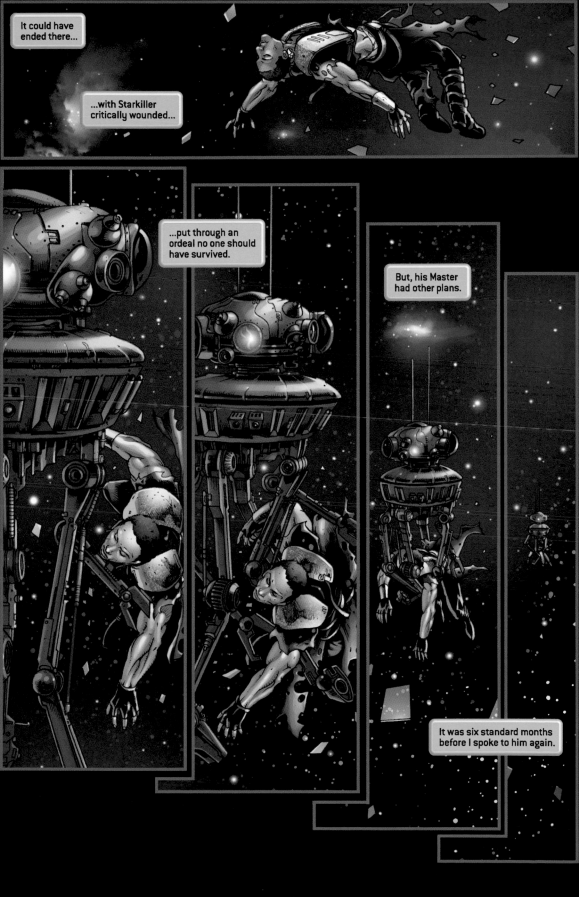

We made our way through the ship, meeting only minimal resistance. But our escape plan was soon compromised...

THE LIFT IS THROUGH HERE, MASTER.

NO...

JUNO!

PROXY! DEACTIVATE THAT THING!

NO SIGN OF ANY PURSUIT. WE'LL SOON BE LIGHT YEARS AWAY FROM ANY IMPERIAL FORCES.

THEN WHAT'S WRONG?

WE HAVE THE ENTIRE GALAXY IN FRONT OF US, AND YET, FOR THE FIRST TIME IN MY LIFE, I DON'T KNOW WHERE TO GO...

I HOPE YOU HAVE A PLAN.

...Starkiller *knew* that they were after Kota.

And that we would need to get to him first.

My Master's only concern was whether or not Kota would recognize him.

But I doubt Kota could even recognize himself.

GENERAL KOTA?

I'VE PAID FOR THIS TABLE. SO WHOEVER YOU ARE, GET LOST.

GENERAL, I'VE TRACKED YOU ACROSS THE GALAXY, FROM NAR SHADDAA TO ZIOST.

I THINK WE CAN HELP EACH OTHER... *JEDI*.

I'M NO JEDI NOW. NOT SINCE *THIS*...

It turns out, carbonite gas makes an excellent weapon.

YOURS IS A FOOL'S ERRAND, BOY. YOU MAY HAVE STOPPED THIS ATTACK, BUT THE EMPEROR'S ARMY IS INFINITE.

YOU'LL EVENTUALLY BE KILLED...OR WORSE. AND NOTHING WILL HAVE CHANGED.

WOULDN'T YOU RATHER DIE FIGHTING THAN DROWN IN SOME CANTINA?

I DON'T KNOW.

BUT I DO HAVE A CONTACT IN THE SENATE WHO CAN USE YOUR LIGHTSABER.

WHERE'S YOUR SHIP?

We arrived on *Kashyyyk* a few days later.

Senator Organa, you already know that Kota brought us to the Wookiee homeworld...

...to find your daughter, though Starkiller would not discover that right away.

But there is part of the mission that you haven't heard yet...

KOTA... I... I THINK I FOUND SOMETHING.

WHAT?

JUST AN OLD HUT... BUT IT FEELS FAMILIAR. I FEEL GREAT DARKNESS HERE. AND SADNESS.

TURN AWAY. GET ON WITH YOUR MISSION.

THERE ARE SOME THINGS YOU AREN'T READY TO FACE.

WHAT'S INSIDE?

HOW SHOULD I KNOW? MY LINK TO THE FORCE HAS BEEN CUT.

BUT IF YOU GO INSIDE, YOU'LL FACE WHATEVER'S IN THERE ALONE.

DON'T LEAVE ME HERE...

I TOLD YOU TO LEAVE IT ALONE, BOY.

When my Master left the hut, I don't think he was *Starkiller* any longer...

He had become something much more *powerful*...

...and more terrifying...

It didn't take Starkiller long to find you, Senator Organa. Maris Brood's use of the dark side drew the Apprentice to the rancor graveyard like a black hole.

RAAAAAWWWR!

But he found far more than he expected...

THIS SHOULD EVEN THE ODDS.

DON'T!

GLIK--

NO!

The rancor was no longer a threat...

...but Maris Brood had learned many tricks from the Felucians.

YOU CAN'T HIDE FROM ME, GIRL.

She used the dark side to bend light around her, to blend in with her surroundings...

...to disappear.

Starkiller told you he would *"meditate"* to find his next target. That wasn't exactly true...

YOUR MISSION GOES WELL, MY APPRENTICE.

I HAVE RECRUITED OTHERS TO MY CAUSE. BUT, NOW I NEED YOUR COUNSEL--

-- MY ALLIES SEEK A MAJOR STRIKE AGAINST THE EMPIRE...

THE EMPEROR RULES THE GALAXY THROUGH FEAR. YOU MUST DESTROY A SYMBOL OF THAT FEAR.

THE EMPIRE IS BUILDING STAR DESTROYERS ABOVE RAXUS PRIME. THAT SHIPYARD IS YOUR NEXT TARGET.

THANK YOU, LORD VADER.

THERE IS MUCH CONFLICT IN YOU.

YOUR FEELINGS FOR YOUR NEW ALLIES ARE GROWING STRONGER. DO NOT FORGET THAT YOU STILL SERVE ME.

UGH. I HATE BEING HIM...

I THINK HE DOES TOO.

I DON'T KNOW IF **ANY** OF US UNDERSTOOD HIM, REALLY.

IT DOESN'T MATTER NOW. WHAT HE DID ON **RAXUS PRIME** WORKED.

IT SHOWED THAT THE EMPIRE **IS** VULNERABLE. IT INSPIRED MY ALLIES AND GALVANIZED THE EMPEROR'S ENEMIES. IT BROUGHT US TOGETHER--

"-- ON CORELLIA."

WE AGREE THAT THE TIME FOR DIPLOMACY AND POLITICS HAS PASSED. IT IS TIME FOR **ACTION.** IF YOU'RE WILLING TO LEAD US, THEN WE'LL JOIN YOUR ALLIANCE.

AS WILL I.

WE SCOURED THE OUTER RIM, BUT EVENTUALLY STARKILLER FOUND THE EMPEROR'S NEW WEAPON...

...THE *DEATH STAR*.

STARKILLER HAD LED ME BACK TO THE *HEART* OF THE EMPIRE.

KEEP THE SHIP CLOAKED AND WAIT BEYOND SCANNER RANGE.

...BUT I THINK HE SAW SOMETHING OF HIMSELF.

THE END

STAR WARS GRAPHIC NOVEL TIMELINE (IN YEARS)

Tales of the Jedi—5,000–3,986 BSW4
Knights of the Old Republic—3,964 BSW4
Jedi vs. Sith—1,000 BSW4
Jedi Council: Acts of War—33 BSW4
Prelude to Rebellion—33 BSW4
Darth Maul—33 BSW4
Episode I: The Phantom Menace—32 BSW4
Outlander—32 BSW4
Emissaries to Malastare—32 BSW4
Jango Fett: Open Seasons—32 BSW4
Twilight—31 BSW4
Bounty Hunters—31 BSW4
The Hunt for Aurra Sing—30 BSW4
Darkness—30 BSW4
The Stark Hyperspace War—30 BSW4
Rite of Passage—28 BSW4
Jango Fett—27 BSW4
Zam Wesell—27 BSW4
Honor and Duty—24 BSW4
Episode II: Attack of the Clones—22 BSW4
Clone Wars—22–19 BSW4
Clone Wars Adventures—22–19 BSW4
General Grievous—20 BSW4
Episode III: Revenge of the Sith—19 BSW4
Dark Times—19 BSW4
Droids—3 BSW4
Boba Fett: Enemy of the Empire—2 BSW4
Underworld—1 BSW4
Episode IV: A New Hope—SW4
Classic Star Wars—0–3 ASW4
A Long Time Ago . . . —0–4 ASW4
Empire—0 ASW4
Rebellion—0 ASW4
Vader's Quest—0 ASW4
Boba Fett: Man with a Mission—0 ASW4
Jabba the Hutt: The Art of the Deal—1 ASW4
Splinter of the Mind's Eye—1 ASW4
Episode V: The Empire Strikes Back—3 ASW4
Shadows of the Empire—3–5 ASW4
Episode VI: Return of the Jedi—4 ASW4
X-Wing Rogue Squadron—4–5 ASW4
Mara Jade: By the Emperor's Hand—4 ASW4
Heir to the Empire—9 ASW4
Dark Force Rising—9 ASW4
The Last Command—9 ASW4
Dark Empire—10 ASW4
Boba Fett: Death, Lies, and Treachery—11 ASW4
Crimson Empire—11 ASW4
Jedi Academy: Leviathan—13 ASW4
Union—20 ASW4
Chewbacca—25 ASW4
Legacy—130 ASW4

Old Republic Era
25,000 – 1000 years before
Star Wars: A New Hope

Rise of the Empire Era
1000 – 0 years before
Star Wars: A New Hope

Rebellion Era
0 – 5 years after
Star Wars: A New Hope

New Republic Era
5 – 25 years after
Star Wars: A New Hope

New Jedi Order Era
25+ years after
Star Wars: A New Hope

Legacy Era
130+ years after
Star Wars: A New Hope

Infinities
Does not apply to timeline

Sergio Aragonés Stomps Star Wars
Star Wars Tales
Star Wars Infinities
Tag and Bink
Star Wars Visionaries

BSW4 = before *Episode IV: A New Hope*. ASW4 = after *Episode IV: A New Hope*.